CONTENT
Multiplication Skills
Grades 2- 4
Designed to reinforce essential math skills!

By completing this math workbook, your child will gain systematic and progressive practice in:

- Recalling Multiplication Facts 1-10
- Testing Multiplication Skills

olour in this picture.

Multiply with Groups

1. **2** groups of **4**

2 x 4 = _____

2. **2** groups of **8**

2 x 8 = _____

3. **3** groups of **6**

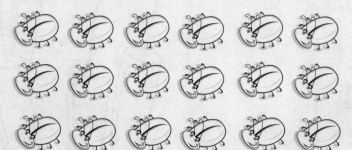

3 x 6 = _____

4. **4** groups of **4**

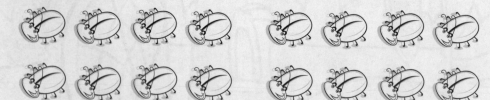

4 x 4 = _____

5. **6** groups of **1**

6 x 1 = _____

Beaver Books Publishing © 2005   Math Book Series

Multiply with Groups

2 groups of **10**

2 x 10 = _____

9 groups of **2**

9 x 2 = _____

8 groups of **5**

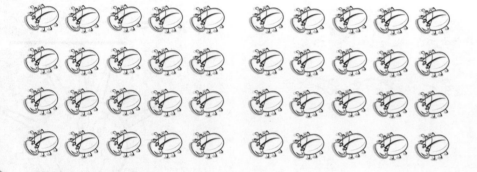

8 x 5 = _____

7 groups of **5**

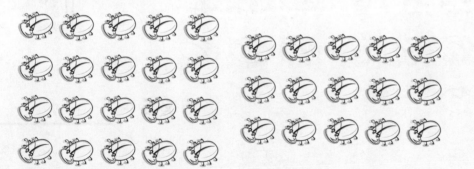

7 x 5 = _____

1 groups of **9**

1 x 9 = _____

Beaver Books Publishing © 2005   Math Book Series

Multiply with Groups

1. 4 groups of 6

4 x 6 = _____

2. 5 groups of 2

5 x 2 = _____

3. 4 groups of 3

4 x 3 = _____

4. 5 groups of 5

5 x 5 = _____

5. 3 groups of 1

3 x 1 = _____

Beaver Books Publishing © 2005   Math Book Series

Multiplication Facts: 0, 1, 2 and 3

Multiplying by 0

Any number multiplied by 0 equals 0.

For example:
6 x 0 = 0

Multiplying by 1

Any number multiplied by 1 equals that number.

For example:
5 x 1 = 5

Multiplying by 2

The multiplication facts for 2 are:

0 x 2 = 0   1 x 2 = 2   2 x 2 = 4   3 x 2 = 6   4 x 2 = 8   5 x 2 = 10

6 x 2 = 12   7 x 2 = 14   8 x 2 = 16   9 x 2 = 18   10 x 2 = 20

Multiplying by 3

The multiplication facts for 3 are:

0 x 3 = 0   1 x 3 = 3   2 x 3 = 6   3 x 3 = 9   4 x 3 = 12   5 x 3 = 15

6 x 3 = 18   7 x 3 = 21   8 x 3 = 24   9 x 3 = 27   10 x 3 = 30

Colour the fish!

Beaver Books Publishing © 2005   Math Book Series

Multiplying by 2

1. **Complete the following multiplication facts.**

$$\begin{array}{r} 6 \\ \times\, 2 \\ \hline \end{array}$$

$$\begin{array}{r} 3 \\ \times\, 2 \\ \hline \end{array}$$

$$\begin{array}{r} 7 \\ \times\, 2 \\ \hline \end{array}$$

$$\begin{array}{r} 4 \\ \times\, 2 \\ \hline \end{array}$$

$$\begin{array}{r} 8 \\ \times\, 2 \\ \hline \end{array}$$

$$\begin{array}{r} 1 \\ \times\, 2 \\ \hline \end{array}$$

$$\begin{array}{r} 5 \\ \times\, 2 \\ \hline \end{array}$$

$$\begin{array}{r} 0 \\ \times\, 2 \\ \hline \end{array}$$

$$\begin{array}{r} 9 \\ \times\, 2 \\ \hline \end{array}$$

$$\begin{array}{r} 2 \\ \times\, 2 \\ \hline \end{array}$$

$$\begin{array}{r} 6 \\ \times\, 2 \\ \hline \end{array}$$

$$\begin{array}{r} 4 \\ \times\, 2 \\ \hline \end{array}$$

$$\begin{array}{r} 8 \\ \times\, 2 \\ \hline \end{array}$$

$$\begin{array}{r} 10 \\ \times\, 2 \\ \hline \end{array}$$

$$\begin{array}{r} 5 \\ \times\, 2 \\ \hline \end{array}$$

Colour me

Beaver Books Publishing © 2005   Math Book Series

Multiplying by 3

Complete the following multiplication facts.

7 × 3	3 × 3	6 × 3	8 × 3	4 × 3

5 × 3	0 × 3	10 × 3	2 × 3

6 × 3	2 × 3	4 × 3

Colour me!

5 × 3	1 × 3	9 × 3

Beaver Books Publishing © 2005   Math Book Series

Multiplying by 1, 2 or 3

1. Complete the following multiplication facts.

7	3	6	8	4
x 2	x 1	x 3	x 1	x 3

5	0	1	10	2
x 2	x 3	x 2	x 2	x 3

6	7	4	2	8
x 1	x 3	x 1	x 2	x 2

1	9	9
x 3	x 1	x 2

More Multiplying by 1, 2 or 3

Colour the correct answer for each multiplication fact, and write it in the blank.

3 x 2 = _____ | 8 | 6 | 2 |

3 x 3 = _____ | 6 | 9 | 12 |

5 x 1 = _____ | 1 | 6 | 5 |

8 x 2 = _____ | 16 | 14 | 18 |

6 x 3 = _____ | 9 | 18 | 16 |

7 x 1 = _____ | 0 | 7 | 8 |

4 x 3 = _____ | 10 | 7 | 12 |

7 x 2 = _____ | 12 | 16 | 14 |

4 x 1 = _____ | 4 | 5 | 6 |

5 x 3 = _____ | 15 | 16 | 10 |

Math Joke:
Q: Why are cows so good at mutliplying numbers?
A: They use a cow-culator!

Colour me!

Beaver Books Publishing © 2005   Math Book Series

Fact Match Up

1. Match the multiplication fact to the correct product.

4 x 1 =

9 x 2 =

3 x 3 =

6 x 1 =

6 x 2 =

7 x 3 =

1 x 1 =

7 x 2 =

10 x 3 =

0 x 1 =

9

12

1

14

4

30

6

0

21

18

4 X 2 =

5 X 5 =

25

8

Colour me!

Beaver Books Publishing © 2005   Math Book Series

Multiplication Facts: 4, 5, and 6

Multiplying by 4

The multiplication facts for 4 are:

$0 \times 4 = 0$ $1 \times 4 = 4$ $2 \times 4 = 8$ $3 \times 4 = 12$ $4 \times 4 = 16$

$5 \times 4 = 20$ $6 \times 4 = 24$ $7 \times 4 = 28$ $8 \times 4 = 32$ $9 \times 4 = 36$

$10 \times 4 = 40$

Multiplying by 5

The multiplication facts for 5 are:

$0 \times 5 = 0$ $1 \times 5 = 5$ $2 \times 5 = 10$ $3 \times 5 = 15$ $4 \times 5 = 20$

$5 \times 5 = 25$ $6 \times 5 = 30$ $7 \times 5 = 35$ $8 \times 5 = 40$ $9 \times 5 = 45$

$10 \times 5 = 50$

Multiplying by 6

The multiplication facts for 6 are:

$0 \times 6 = 0$ $1 \times 6 = 6$ $2 \times 6 = 12$ $3 \times 6 = 18$ $4 \times 6 = 24$

$5 \times 6 = 30$ $6 \times 6 = 36$ $7 \times 6 = 42$ $8 \times 6 = 48$ $9 \times 6 = 54$

$10 \times 6 = 60$

Colour the bees and flower!

Beaver Books Publishing © 2005   Math Book Series

Multiplying by 4

1. Complete the following multiplication facts.

$$\begin{array}{c} 6 \\ \times\,4 \end{array} \qquad \begin{array}{c} 3 \\ \times\,4 \end{array} \qquad \begin{array}{c} 7 \\ \times\,4 \end{array} \qquad \begin{array}{c} 4 \\ \times\,4 \end{array} \qquad \begin{array}{c} 8 \\ \times\,4 \end{array}$$

$$\begin{array}{c} 10 \\ \times\,4 \end{array} \qquad \begin{array}{c} 5 \\ \times\,4 \end{array} \qquad \begin{array}{c} 0 \\ \times\,4 \end{array} \qquad \begin{array}{c} 9 \\ \times\,4 \end{array}$$

$$\begin{array}{c} 2 \\ \times\,4 \end{array} \qquad \begin{array}{c} 6 \\ \times\,4 \end{array} \qquad \begin{array}{c} 4 \\ \times\,4 \end{array}$$

$$\begin{array}{c} 8 \\ \times\,4 \end{array} \qquad \begin{array}{c} 1 \\ \times\,4 \end{array} \qquad \begin{array}{c} 5 \\ \times\,4 \end{array}$$

Multiplying by 5

Complete the following multiplication facts.

7	3	6	8	4
x 5	x 5	x 5	x 5	x 5

5	0	10	9
x 5	x 5	x 5	x 5

6	2	4
x 5	x 5	x 5

5	1	9
x 5	x 5	x 5

Colour me!

Beaver Books Publishing © 2005   Math Book Series

Multiplying by 6

1. Complete the following multiplication facts.

6	3	7	4	8
x 6	x 6	x 6	x 6	x 6

10	5	0	9
x 6	x 6	x 6	x 6

2	6	4
x 6	x 6	x 6

8	1	5
x 6	x 6	x 6

Colour me!

Beaver Books Publishing © 2005   Math Book Series

Multiplying by 4, 5 or 6

Complete the following multiplication facts.

7 x 5	3 x 4	6 x 6	8 x 5	10 x 4

5 x 6	0 x 6	1 x 4	2 x 5	1 x 5

6 x 4	2 x 6	4 x 4	7 x 6	2 x 4

1 x 6	9 x 5	9 x 4

Beaver Books Publishing © 2005   Math Book Series

More Multiplying by 4, 5 or 6

Colour the correct answer for each multiplication fact, and write it in the blank.

5 x 4 = _____ 　 **18** **20** **22**

2 x 5 = _____ 　 **12** **7** **10**

7 x 6 = _____ 　 **42** **44** **40**

2 x 4 = _____ 　 **8** **6** **10**

7 x 5 = _____ 　 **45** **35** **40**

0 x 6 = _____ 　 **1** **6** **0**

8 x 4 = _____ 　 **32** **30** **28**

1 x 5 = _____ 　 **5** **6** **1**

9 x 6 = _____ 　 **52** **56** **54**

6 x 4 = _____ 　 **24** **26** **28**

Q: Why did the teacher wear sunglasses to school?
A: Her students were all really bright!

Colour us!

Beaver Books Publishing © 2005 　 Math Book Series

Fact Match Up

Match the multiplication fact to the correct product.

9 x 4 =

8 x 5 =

8 x 6 =

5 x 4 =

6 x 5 =

0 x 6 =

3 x 4 =

5 x 5 =

10 x 6 =

8 x 4 =

(48)
(0)
(30)
(12)
(60)
(25)
(36)
(32)
(20)
(40)

4 X 1 =

6 X 2 =

Colour me!

Beaver Books Publishing © 2005   Math Book Series

Multiplication Facts: 7, 8, and 9

1. **Multiplying by 7**

The multiplication facts for 7 are:

$0 \times 7 = 0$ $1 \times 7 = 7$ $2 \times 7 = 14$ $3 \times 7 = 21$ $4 \times 7 = 28$

$5 \times 7 = 35$ $6 \times 7 = 42$ $7 \times 7 = 49$ $8 \times 7 = 56$ $9 \times 7 = 63$

$10 \times 7 = 70$

2. **Multiplying by 8**

The multiplication facts for 8 are:

$0 \times 8 = 0$ $1 \times 8 = 8$ $2 \times 8 = 16$ $3 \times 8 = 24$ $4 \times 8 = 32$

$5 \times 8 = 40$ $6 \times 8 = 48$ $7 \times 8 = 56$ $8 \times 8 = 64$ $9 \times 8 = 72$

$10 \times 8 = 80$

3. **Multiplying by 9**

The multiplication facts for 9 are:

$0 \times 9 = 0$ $1 \times 9 = 9$ $2 \times 9 = 18$ $3 \times 9 = 27$ $4 \times 9 = 36$

$5 \times 9 = 45$ $6 \times 9 = 54$ $7 \times 9 = 63$ $8 \times 9 = 72$ $9 \times 9 = 81$

$10 \times 9 = 90$

Colour the mice and the piece of cheese!

Beaver Books Publishing © 2005   Math Book Series

Multiplying by 7

Complete the following multiplication facts.

7	3	6	8	4
x 7	x 7	x 7	x 7	x 7

5	0	10	2
x 7	x 7	x 7	x 7

6	2	4
x 7	x 7	x 7

5	1	9
x 7	x 7	x 7

Colour me!

Beaver Books Publishing © 2005   Math Book Series

Multiplying by 8

1. Complete the following multiplication facts.

$$\begin{array}{c} 3 \\ \times\, 8 \\ \hline \end{array} \qquad \begin{array}{c} 7 \\ \times\, 8 \\ \hline \end{array} \qquad \begin{array}{c} 8 \\ \times\, 8 \\ \hline \end{array} \qquad \begin{array}{c} 6 \\ \times\, 8 \\ \hline \end{array} \qquad \begin{array}{c} 4 \\ \times\, 8 \\ \hline \end{array}$$

$$\begin{array}{c} 0 \\ \times\, 8 \\ \hline \end{array} \qquad \begin{array}{c} 5 \\ \times\, 8 \\ \hline \end{array} \qquad \begin{array}{c} 3 \\ \times\, 8 \\ \hline \end{array} \qquad \begin{array}{c} 1 \\ \times\, 8 \\ \hline \end{array}$$

$$\begin{array}{c} 9 \\ \times\, 8 \\ \hline \end{array} \qquad \begin{array}{c} 4 \\ \times\, 8 \\ \hline \end{array} \qquad \begin{array}{c} 2 \\ \times\, 8 \\ \hline \end{array}$$

$$\begin{array}{c} 8 \\ \times\, 8 \\ \hline \end{array} \qquad \begin{array}{c} 5 \\ \times\, 8 \\ \hline \end{array} \qquad \begin{array}{c} 10 \\ \times\, 8 \\ \hline \end{array}$$

Colour me!

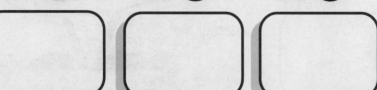

Multiplying by 9

Complete the following multiplication facts.

4 x 9	8 x 9	6 x 9	3 x 9	7 x 9

2 x 9	0 x 9	10 x 9	5 x 9

7 x 9	2 x 9	6 x 9

9 x 9	5 x 9	1 x 9

Colour me!

Beaver Books Publishing © 2005   Math Book Series

Multiplying by 7, 8 or 9

1. Complete the following multiplication facts.

7 x 7	3 x 8	10 x 9	8 x 8	4 x 7

5 x 9	0 x 7	1 x 7	2 x 8	1 x 8

6 x 9	7 x 9	4 x 8	2 x 7	2 x 9

1 x 9	9 x 8	9 x 9

Beaver Books Publishing © 2005   Math Book Series

More Multiplying by 7, 8 or 9

Colour the correct answer for each multiplication fact, and write it in the blank.

8 x 7 = _____ | 52 | 54 | 56 |

2 x 8 = _____ | 12 | 16 | 10 |

9 x 9 = _____ | 78 | 81 | 82 |

5 x 7 = _____ | 35 | 32 | 30 |

3 x 8 = _____ | 28 | 22 | 24 |

2 x 9 = _____ | 18 | 16 | 12 |

7 x 7 = _____ | 47 | 49 | 52 |

0 x 8 = _____ | 0 | 8 | 1 |

3 x 9 = _____ | 27 | 26 | 32 |

4 x 7 = _____ | 24 | 26 | 28 |

Colour us!

Beaver Books Publishing © 2005   Math Book Series

Fact Match Up

1. Match the multiplication fact to the correct product.

5 x 7 =

7 x 8 =

10 x 9 =

4 x 7 =

6 x 8 =

1 x 9 =

2 x 7 =

8 x 8 =

3 x 9 =

9 x 7 =

27	 3 X 7 =
14	
48	8 X 1 =
35	
63	
56	
90	
9	
28	Colour me!
64	

21

24

Multiplication with 10

Multiplying by 10

The multiplication facts for 10 are:

$0 \times 10 = 0$ $1 \times 10 = 10$ $2 \times 10 = 20$ $3 \times 10 = 30$ $4 \times 10 = 40$

$5 \times 10 = 50$ $6 \times 10 = 60$ $7 \times 10 = 70$ $8 \times 10 = 80$ $9 \times 10 = 90$

$10 \times 10 = 100$

Q: What do you call a computer superhero?
A: A Screen Saver!

Q: How many rocks can you put into any empty bucket?
A: Only one, after that the bucket isn't empty!

Colour me!

Beaver Books Publishing © 2005   Math Book Series

Multiplying by 10

Complete the following multiplication facts.

3	7	8	6	4
x 10	x 10	x 10	x 10	x 10

0	5	2	1
x 10	x 10	x 10	x 10

3	4	2
x 10	x 10	x 10

9	5	10
x 10	x 10	x 10

Colour me!

Fact Match Up

Match the multiplication fact to the correct product.

5 x 10 =

1 x 10 =

4 x 10 =

2 x 10 =

6 x 10 =

10 x 10 =

9 x 10 =

8 x 10 =

3 x 10 =

7 x 10 =

100

60

90

30

50

70

80

10

40

20

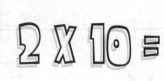

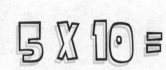

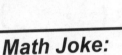

Math Joke:

Q: What goes up and never goes down?
A: Your age!

Colour me!

27

What do people do in clock factories?

1. Solve the multiplication facts to find out.

4 x 6 = (　　　　) D   2 x 4 = (　　　　) E

3 x 4 = (　　　　) Y   4 x 5 = (　　　　) M

6 x 10 = (　　　　) A   4 x 4 = (　　　　) C

5 x 1 = (　　　　) L   2 x 2 = (　　　　) F

5 x 8 = (　　　　) K   6 x 6 = (　　　　) H

6 x 3 = (　　　　) S   3 x 5 = (　　　　) T

___ ___ ___ ___ / ___ ___ ___ ___ /
15   36   8   12   20   60   40   8

___ ___ ___ ___ ___ / ___ ___ ___ /
4   60   16   8   18   60   5   5

___ ___ ___ •
24   60   12

Math Joke:

Q: How many months have 28 days?
A: All of them!

Colour me!

Why do spiders love computers?

Solve the multiplication facts to find out.

8 x 1 = (   ) H   2 x 5 = (   ) V

10 x 5 = (   ) I   2 x 10 = (   ) E

9 x 8 = (   ) B   4 x 8 = (   ) S

7 x 5 = (   ) T   10 x 6 = (   ) A

3 x 2 = (   ) W   2 x 7 = (   ) Y

___ ___ ___ ___ / ___ ___ ___ ___ /
35   8   20   14   8   60   10   20

___ ___ ___ / ___ ___ ___ ___ /
35   8   20   72   20   32   35

___ ___ ___ ___ ___ ___ ___ ___ .
6   20   72   32   50   35   20   32

Math Joke:
Q: Which weighs more? A kg of flour or a kg of feathers?
A: They both weigh the same!

Colour me!

Beaver Books Publishing © 2005   Math Book Series

What has four wheels and flies?

Solve the multiplication facts to find out.

9 x 5 = (   ) B   10 x 9 = (   ) U

1 x 6 = (   ) T   2 x 4 = (   ) G

8 x 3 = (   ) C   7 x 1 = (   ) K

3 x 6 = (   ) A   0 x 5 = (   ) R

6 x 9 = (   ) E

___ / ___ ___ ___ ___ ___ ___ ___ /
18   8   18   0   45   18   8   54

___ ___ ___ ___ ___ !
6   0   90   24   7

Math Joke:

Q: What tool do you use in math?
A: Multi-pliers!

Colour me!

What did the bubble gum say to the sneaker?

Solve the multiplication facts to find out.

5 x 5 = (   ) A

9 x 7 = (   ) S

2 x 8 = (   ) U

3 x 7 = (   ) K

8 x 8 = (   ) I

2 x 6 = (   ) O

2 x 2 = (   ) T

7 x 10 = (   ) C

2 x 5 = (   ) M

5 x 10 = (   ) N

3 x 1 = (   ) Y

___ / ___ ___ / ___ ___ ___ ___ ___ /
64   25   10   63 4 16 70 21

___ ___ / ___ ___ ___ !
12 50   3 12 16

Math Joke:

Q: Who was the first math student?
A: Add-em (Adam)!

Colour me!

Beaver Books Publishing © 2005   Math Book Series

Double the Fun

1. Complete the following multiplication facts.

8	2	10	3	4
x 8	x 2	x 10	x 3	x 4

5	6	9	1	5
x 5	x 6	x 9	x 1	x 5

7	8	4	6	2
x 7	x 8	x 4	x 6	x 2

1	9	4
x 1	x 9	x 4

Beaver Books Publishing © 2005   Math Book Series

Fact Match Up

Match the multiplication fact to the correct product.

4 x 2 =

3 x 8 =

5 x 5 =

9 x 9 =

7 x 2 =

8 x 8 =

10 x 3 =

8 x 5 =

9 x 7 =

4 x 4 =

8

25

16

24

14

63

40

64

81

30

Math Joke:

Q: Who invented fractions?
A: Henry the 1/8th!

Colour me!

33

Multiplication Test

1. Complete the following multiplication facts.

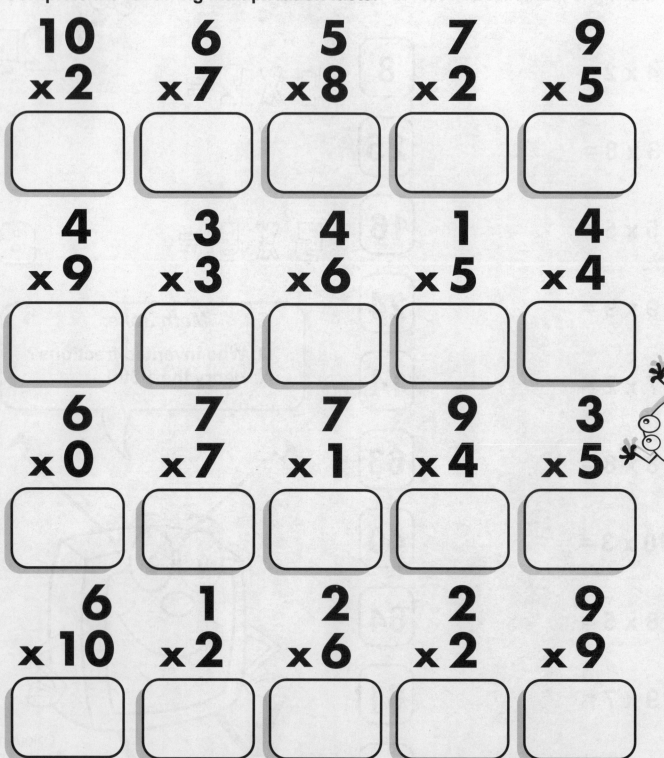

10 × 2	6 × 7	5 × 8	7 × 2	9 × 5
4 × 9	3 × 3	4 × 6	1 × 5	4 × 4
6 × 0	7 × 7	7 × 1	9 × 4	3 × 5
6 × 10	1 × 2	2 × 6	2 × 2	9 × 9

How many did you get right? _____ out of 20.

Beaver Books Publishing © 2005   Math Book Series

Multiplication Test

Complete the following multiplication facts.

0	10	5	2	1
x 4	x 3	x 5	x 9	x 0

7	9	8	4	3
x 3	x 4	x 0	x 3	x 3

8	3	10	1	4
x 5	x 2	x 9	x 5	x 8

8	8	2	3	5
x 1	x 8	x 7	x 6	x 2

How many did you get right? _____ out of 20.

Multiplication Test

Complete the following multiplication facts.

5 x 5	1 x 6	10 x 4	7 x 8	5 x 0
5 x 7	5 x 9	8 x 10	4 x 2	4 x 5
3 x 6	8 x 9	3 x 10	3 x 8	2 x 6
4 x 7	1 x 5	2 x 7	4 x 3	7 x 2

How many did you get right? _____ out of 20.

Beaver Books Publishing © 2005   Math Book Series

Multiplication Test

Complete the following multiplication facts.

7	9	10	1	5
x 5	x 2	x 6	x 1	x 2

6	8	5	1	4
x 3	x 9	x 10	x 2	x 4

8	8	10	1	3
x 6	x 8	x 4	x 4	x 3

4	2	5	9	6
x 9	x 7	x 4	x 6	x 6

How many did you get right? _____ out of 20.

Multiplication Table

1. Below is the multiplication table to help you.

X	0	1	2	3	4	5	6	7	8	9	10
0	0	0	0	0	0	0	0	0	0	0	0
1	0	1	2	3	4	5	6	7	8	9	10
2	0	2	4	6	8	10	12	14	16	18	20
3	0	3	6	9	12	15	18	21	24	27	30
4	0	4	8	12	16	20	24	28	32	36	40
5	0	5	10	15	20	25	30	35	40	45	50
6	0	6	12	18	24	30	36	42	48	54	60
7	0	7	14	21	28	35	42	49	56	63	70
8	0	8	16	24	32	40	48	56	64	72	80
9	0	9	18	27	36	45	54	63	72	81	90
10	0	10	20	30	40	50	60	70	80	90	100

Q: Why do baby goats know how to multiply?
A: Because they are smart kids!

Beaver Books Publishing © 2005   Math Book Series

Answer Pages

Page 2. 2 x 4 = (8)   2 x 8 = (16)   3 x 6 = (18)   4 x 4 = (16)   6 x 1 = (6)

Page 3. 2 x 10 = (20)   9 x 2 = (18)   8 x 5 = (40)   7 x 5 = (35)   1 x 9 = (9)

Page 4. 4 x 6 = (24)   5 x 2 = (10)   4 x 3 = (12)   5 x 5 = (25)   3 x 1 = (3)

Page 6.
6 x 2 = (12)   3 x 2 = (6)   7 x 2 = (14)   4 x 2 = (8)   8 x 2 = (16)
1 x 2 = (2)   5 x 2 = (10)   0 x 2 = (0)   9 x 2 = (18)   2 x 2 = (4)
6 x 2 = (12)   4 x 2 = (8)   8 x 2 = (16)   10 x 2 = (20)   5 x 2 = (10)

Page 7.
7 x 3 = (21)   3 x 3 = (9)   6 x 3 = (18)   8 x 3 = (24)   4 x 3 = (12)
5 x 3 = (15)   0 x 3 = (0)   10 x 3 = (30)   2 x 3 = (6)   6 x 3 = (18)
2 x 3 = (6)   4 x 3 = (12)   5 x 3 = (15)   1 x 3 = (3)   9 x 3 = (27)

Page 8.
7 x 2 = (14)   3 x 1 = (3)   6 x 3 = (18)   8 x 1 = (8)   4 x 3 = (12)
5 x 2 = (10)   0 x 3 = (0)   1 x 2 = (2)   10 x 2 = (20)   2 x 3 = (6)
6 x 1 = (6)   7 x 3 = (21)   4 x 1 = (4)   2 x 2 = (4)   8 x 2 = (16)
1 x 3 = (3)   9 x 1 = (9)   9 x 2 = (18)

Page 9.
3 x 2 = (6)   3 x 3 = (9)   5 x 1 = (5)   8 x 2 = (16)   6 x 3 = (18)
7 x 1 = (7)   4 x 3 = (12)   7 x 2 = (14)   4 x 1 = (4)   5 x 3 = (15)

Page 10.
4 x 1 = (4)   9 x 2 = (18)   3 x 3 = (9)   6 x 1 = (6)   6 x 2 = (12)
7 x 3 = (21)   1 x 1 = (1)   7 x 2 = (14)   10 x 3 = (30)   0 x 1 = (0)

Page 12.
6 x 4 = (24)   3 x 4 = (12)   7 x 4 = (28)   4 x 4 = (16)   8 x 4 = (32)
10 x 4 = (40)   5 x 4 = (20)   0 x 4 = (0)   9 x 4 = (36)   2 x 4 = (8)
6 x 4 = (24)   4 x 4 = (16)   8 x 4 = (32)   1 x 4 = (4)   5 x 4 = (20)

Answer Pages

Page 13.

7 x 5 = (35)	3 x 5 = (15)	6 x 5 = (30)	8 x 5 = (40)	4 x 5 = (20)
5 x 5 = (25)	0 x 5 = (0)	10 x 5 = (50)	9 x 5 = (45)	6 x 5 = (30)
2 x 5 = (10)	4 x 5 = (20)	5 x 5 = (25)	1 x 5 = (5)	9 x 5 = (45)

Page 14.

6 x 6 = (36)	3 x 6 = (18)	7 x 6 = (42)	4 x 6 = (24)	8 x 6 = (48)
10 x 6 = (60)	5 x 6 = (30)	0 x 6 = (0)	9 x 6 = (54)	2 x 6 = (12)
6 x 6 = (36)	4 x 6 = (24)	8 x 6 = (48)	1 x 6 = (6)	5 x 6 = (30)

Page 15.

7 x 5 = (35)	3 x 4 = (12)	6 x 6 = (36)	8 x 5 = (40)	10 x 4 = (40)
5 x 6 = (30)	0 x 6 = (0)	1 x 4 = (4)	2 x 5 = (10)	1 x 5 = (5)
6 x 4 = (24)	2 x 6 = (12)	4 x 4 = (16)	7 x 6 = (42)	2 x 4 = (8)
1 x 6 = (6)	9 x 5 = (45)	9 x 4 = (36)		

Page 16.

5 x 4 = (20)	2 x 5 = (10)	7 x 6 = (42)	2 x 4 = (8)	7 x 5 = (35)
0 x 6 = (0)	8 x 4 = (32)	1 x 5 = (5)	9 x 6 = (54)	6 x 4 = (24)

Page 17.

9 x 4 = (36)	8 x 5 = (40)	8 x 6 = (48)	5 x 4 = (20)	6 x 5 = (30)
0 x 6 = (0)	3 x 4 = (12)	5 x 5 = (25)	10 x 6 = (60)	8 x 4 = (32)

Page 19.

7 x 7 = (49)	3 x 7 = (21)	6 x 7 = (42)	8 x 7 = (56)	4 x 7 = (28)
5 x 7 = (35)	0 x 7 = (0)	10 x 7 = (70)	2 x 7 = (14)	6 x 7 = (42)
2 x 7 = (14)	4 x 7 = (28)	5 x 7 = (35)	1 x 7 = (7)	9 x 7 = (63)

Page 20.

3 x 8 = (24)	7 x 8 = (56)	8 x 8 = (64)	6 x 8 = (48)	4 x 8 = (32)
0 x 8 = (0)	5 x 8 = (40)	3 x 8 = (24)	1 x 8 = (8)	9 x 8 = (72)
4 x 8 = (32)	2 x 8 = (16)	8 x 8 = (64)	5 x 8 = (40)	10 x 8 = (80)

Page 21.

4 x 9 = (36)	8 x 9 = (72)	6 x 9 = (54)	3 x 9 = (27)	7 x 9 = (63)
2 x 9 = (18)	0 x 9 = (0)	10 x 9 = (90)	5 x 9 = (45)	7 x 9 = (63)
2 x 9 = (18)	6 x 9 = (54)	9 x 9 = (81)	5 x 9 = (45)	1 x 9 = (9)

Beaver Books Publishing © 2005   Math Book Series

Answer Pages

Page 22.

7 x 7 = (49)   3 x 8 = (24)   10 x 9 = (90)   8 x 8 = (64)   4 x 7 = (28)

5 x 9 = (45)   0 x 7 = (0)   1 x 7 = (7)   2 x 8 = (16)   1 x 8 = (8)

6 x 9 = (54)   7 x 9 = (63)   4 x 8 = (32)   2 x 7 = (14)   2 x 9 = (18)

1 x 9 = (9)   9 x 8 = (72)   9 x 9 = (81)

Page 23.

8 x 7 = (56)   2 x 8 = (16)   9 x 9 = (81)   5 x 7 = (35)   3 x 8 = (24)

2 x 9 = (18)   7 x 7 = (49)   0 x 8 = (0)   3 x 9 = (27)   4 x 7 = (28)

Page 24.

5 x 7 = (35)   7 x 8 = (56)   10 x 9 = (90)   4 x 7 = (28)   6 x 8 = (48)

1 x 9 = (9)   2 x 7 = (14)   8 x 8 = (64)   3 x 9 = (27)   9 x 7 = (63)

Page 26.

3 x 10 = (30)   7 x 10 = (70)   8 x 10 = (80)   6 x 10 = (60)   4 x 10 = (40)

0 x 10 = (0)   5 x 10 = (50)   2 x 10 = (20)   1 x 10 = (10)   3 x 10 = (30)

4 x 10 = (40)   2 x 10 = (20)   9 x 10 = (90)   5 x 10 = (50)   10 x 10 = (100)

Page 27.

5 x 10 = (50)   1 x 10 = (10)   4 x 10 = (40)   2 x 10 = (20)   6 x 10 = (60)

10 x 10 = (100)   9 x 10 = (90)   8 x 10 = (80)   3 x 10 = (30)   7 x 10 = (70)

Page 28.

4 x 6 = (24)D   2 x 4 = (8)E   6 x 10 = (60)A   4 x 4 = (16)C

3 x 4 = (12)Y   4 x 5 = (20)M   5 x 1 = (5)L   2 x 2 = (4)F

5 x 8 = (40)K   6 x 6 = (36)H   6 x 3 = (18)S   3 x 5 = (15)T

Answer: They make faces all day.

Page 29.

8 x 1 = (8)H   10 x 5 = (50)I   9 x 8 = (72)B   2 x 5 = (10)V

7 x 5 = (35)T   3 x 2 = (6)W   2 x 10 = (20)E   4 x 8 = (32)S

10 x 6 = (60)A   2 x 7 = (14)Y

Answer: They have the best websites!

Beaver Books Publishing © 2005   **Math Book Series**

Answer Pages

Page 30.

9 x 5 = (45) B   3 x 6 = (18) A   10 x 9 = (90) U

1 x 6 = (6) T   6 x 9 = (54) E   2 x 4 = (8) G

8 x 3 = (24) C   7 x 1 = (7) K   0 x 5 = (0) R

Answer: A garbage truck!

Page 31.

5 x 5 = (25) A   2 x 6 = (12) O   2 x 5 = (10) M

9 x 7 = (63) S   2 x 2 = (4) T   5 x 10 = (50) N

2 x 8 = (16) U   7 x 10 = (70) C   3 x 1 = (3) Y

3 x 7 = (21) K   8 x 8 = (64) I

Answer: I am stuck on you.

Page 32.

8 x 8 = (64)   2 x 2 = (4)   10 x 10 = (100)   3 x 3 = (9)   4 x 4 = (16)

5 x 5 = (25)   6 x 6 = (36)   9 x 9 = (81)   1 x 1 = (1)   5 x 5 = (25)

7 x 7 = (49)   8 x 8 = (64)   4 x 4 = (16)   6 x 6 = (36)   2 x 2 = (4)

1 x 1 = (1)   9 x 9 = (81)   4 x 4 = (16)

Page 33.

4 x 2 = (8)   3 x 8 = (24)   5 x 5 = (25)   9 x 9 = (81)   7 x 2 = (14)

8 x 8 = (64)   10 x 3 = (30)   8 x 5 = (40)   9 x 7 = (63)   4 x 4 = (16)

Page 34.

10 x 2 = (20)   6 x 7 = (42)   5 x 8 = (40)   7 x 2 = (14)   9 x 5 = (45)

4 x 9 = (36)   3 x 3 = (9)   4 x 6 = (24)   1 x 5 = (5)   4 x 4 = (16)

6 x 0 = (0)   7 x 7 = (49)   7 x 1 = (7)   9 x 4 = (36)   3 x 5 = (15)

6 x 10 = (60)   1 x 2 = (2)   2 x 6 = (12)   2 x 2 = (4)   9 x 9 = (81)

Beaver Books Publishing © 2005   Math Book Series

Answer Pages

Page 35.

0 x 4 = (0)	10 x 3 = (30)	5 x 5 = (25)	2 x 9 = (18)	1 x 0 = (0)
7 x 3 = (21)	9 x 4 = (36)	8 x 0 = (0)	4 x 3 = (12)	3 x 3 = (9)
8 x 5 = (40)	3 x 2 = (6)	10 x 9 = (90)	1 x 5 = (5)	4 x 8 = (32)
8 x 1 = (8)	8 x 8 = (64)	2 x 7 = (14)	3 x 6 = (18)	5 x 2 = (10)

Page 36.

5 x 5 = (25)	1 x 6 = (6)	10 x 4 = (40)	7 x 8 = (56)	5 x 0 = (0)
5 x 7 = (35)	5 x 9 = (45)	8 x 10 = (80)	4 x 2 = (8)	4 x 5 = (20)
3 x 6 = (18)	8 x 9 = (72)	3 x 10 = (30)	3 x 8 = (24)	2 x 6 = (12)
4 x 7 = (28)	1 x 5 = (5)	2 x 7 = (14)	4 x 3 = (12)	7 x 2 = (14)

Page 37.

7 x 5 = (35)	9 x 2 = (18)	10 x 6 = (60)	1 x 1 = (1)	5 x 2 = (10)
6 x 3 = (18)	8 x 9 = (72)	5 x 10 = (50)	1 x 2 = (2)	4 x 4 = (16)
8 x 6 = (48)	8 x 8 = (64)	10 x 4 = (40)	1 x 4 = (4)	3 x 3 = (9)
4 x 9 = (36)	2 x 7 = (14)	5 x 4 = (20)	9 x 6 = (54)	6 x 6 = (36)

Math Joke:

Q. What did the math book say to the student?
A. I have a lot of problems.

Colour me!

Beaver Books Publishing © 2005   Math Book Series

BEAVER BOOKS

Certificate of Completion.

Well Done!

You are Great!

Name:
_____